THIS IS ME!

CREATIVE STARS

Edited By Roseanna Caswell

First published in Great Britain in 2022 by:

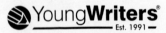 YoungWriters®
—— Est. 1991 ——

Young Writers
Remus House
Coltsfoot Drive
Peterborough
PE2 9BF
Telephone: 01733 890066
Website: www.youngwriters.co.uk

Printed and bound in the UK by BookPrintingUK
Website: www.bookprintinguk.com
YB0491C

FOREWORD

For Young Writers' latest competition This Is Me,
we asked primary school pupils to look inside
themselves, to think about what makes them unique,
and then write a poem about it! They rose to the
challenge magnificently and the result is this fantastic
collection of poems in a variety of poetic styles.

Here at Young Writers our aim is to encourage creativity
in children and to inspire a love of the written word, so
it's great to get such an amazing response, with some
absolutely fantastic poems. It's important for children to
focus on and celebrate themselves and this competition
allowed them to write freely and honestly, celebrating
what makes them great, expressing their hopes and
fears, or simply writing about their favourite things.
This Is Me gave them the power of words. The result
is a collection of inspirational and moving poems that
also showcase their creativity and writing ability.

I'd like to congratulate all the young poets
in this anthology, I hope this inspires them
to continue with their creative writing.

CONTENTS

Audenshaw Primary School, Audenshaw

Scarlett Rose Mcguire (9)	1
Robyn Scarratt (9)	2
Lucy May Walton (9)	4
Katie Clowrey (9)	5

Beehive Preparatory School, Redbridge

Axia Reid-Vickers (8)	6
Samveer Dhani (8)	7
Zachariah Qureshi (9)	8
Awais Mohammed Adam (8)	9
Javeria Chaudhry (8)	10
Dawud Shah (7)	11

Bentinck Primary & Nursery School, Nottingham

Shareen Islam	12
Horia Noori	14
Zoya Hussain	16
Eiliyah Ahad	17
Hijran Zia	18
Amalie-Rose Williams (10)	20
Aroua Serief (10)	21
Haseeb Babar (10)	22
Aya Chebli	23
Ali Bashir	24
Ewa Petelska (11)	25
Muhammad Hashim Shahyan (7)	26
Sohana Sheza (7)	27
Maariya Mehmood (7)	28
Emmanuel Mecha (7)	29

Kovan Salih Graham	30
Arham Babar (7)	31
Eliza Yasin (7)	32

Bonner Primary School, Mile End

Maryam Nessa (9)	33
Aqsa Shahab (9)	34
Qazi Tashfeen Ehsan (9)	36
Jannah Hussain (9)	38
Ikram Ali (9)	40
Muhammed Ayaan Islam (9)	41

Downsend School, Leatherhead

Isabella Ava Cross (10)	42
Emma Clarke (10)	43
Emilia Davies (10)	44
Jessica Ribet (10)	46
Sheung Yu Ryanna Ng (10)	47
Jasmine Droutis (10)	48
Holly Dada (10)	49
Harriet Hughes (10)	50
Lucy Guiney (10)	51
Ryan Dekker (10)	52
Ethan Chan (10)	53
Chloe Della (11)	54
Ria Kaur Sandhu (10)	55
Elliot Moore (10)	56
Marcus Young (10)	57
George Gale (10)	58
Tayla Smith (10)	59
Stanley Davenport (11)	60
Oscar Manly (10)	61
Esme Rodulfo-Flatt (10)	62
George Dale (10)	63

Amelie Chellun (10) 64
Billy Maylin (10) 65
Raffy Fewings (10) 66
Sam Russell (10) 67

Langcraigs Primary School, Glenburn

David Mason (9) 68
Ethan McCafferty (10) 69
Charlie McLaren (9) 70
Daniel McGregor (8) 71
Lucy Robertson (9) 72
Hannah Scott (10) 73
Orlay McEnhill (9) 74
Ellis Adams (8) 75
Ellie Jane Longwill (10) 76
Lauren Thomson (9) 77
Heather Nicholson (8) 78
Ellis Duffin (10) 79
Aimee Dunn (10) 80
Reid Hughes (9) 81
Riley Higginson (9) 82
Arwen Bowskill (10) 83
Ronnie Millar (10) 84
Romy Easdon (10) 85

Seaview Primary School, Belfast

Gifty Ezirike (11) 86
Anna McComb 88
Carter Whyte (11) 89
Hsuan-Jui Chang (11) 90
Corey-Dede Kirkland (10) 92
Faith Mcalorum (10) 93
Phoenix Blayney (10) 94
Lilith Maguire (11) 95
Esmee Manton (10) 96
Boye Li (11) 98
Lexi Harker Quin (11) 99
Jake McKinley (10) 100
Abir Khan 101
Mikolaj 102
Caleb Smyth (10) 104

Maja Skwiercz (10) 105
Saskia McLaughlin 106
Twinkle Chen (11) 107
Harry McKee (11) 108
Lewis Mackle (11) 109
Dragos Petras (11) 110
Yazmin Akay (11) 111
Aaron McMullan 112
Olivia Doherty (10) 113
Amelia Gogacz (10) 114

St Thomas Cantilupe CE Primary, Hereford

Sian Bevan (10) 115
Phoebe Parry (10) 116
Natasha Ingram (10) 118
Rhian Oldaker (10) 120
Mila Tomev (10) 121
Ashton Brown (10) 122
Flynn Beard (11) 123
Adeoluwa Amos (8) 124
Bruno Janusz (8) 125
Bella Hall (8) 126
Olivia Racis (8) 127
Liam Jones (10) 128
Lola Jane Carlson (8) 129
Olivia Underhill (9) 130
Jaya Shellam (9) 131
Alan Podgorski (8) 132
Cobie Jackson (8) 133
Fabian Rucki (9) 134
Maria Tomev (8) 135
Alarna Lloyd (8) 136
Arshya Sanju (8) 137
Oliver Zheng (8) 138
Julia Koleczek (9) 139
Gina Tangiaritsakul (8) 140
Mariana Campos (8) 141
Eint Myat (8) 142
Ted Waters (8) 143
Rio Whittingham (9) 144

West Ashton Primary School, West Ashton

Beth Williams (11)	145
Deni Donovan (11)	146
Abigail Squires (10)	149
Isabel Hinds (9)	150
Melody Turner (9)	152
Keilani McOwan (10)	154
Coco Jones (10)	156
Rose Stower-Draper (10)	158
Elsie Dewsbury (9)	159
Nicola Plant (9)	160
Jacob Squires (10)	161
Isabelle Foo (10)	162
Owen Squires (10)	163
Maia Hobbs (10)	164
Jasmine Molloy (11)	165
Georgia Draper (10)	166
Cameron Earl-Burke (9)	167
Arthur Thomas-Busow (9)	168
Poppy Self (10)	169
Tilly Lewis (10)	170
Jack Le Grys (10)	171
Jaime Noad (10)	172
Harry Prichard (10)	173
Evelyn Morris (10)	174
Kyra Husk (10)	175
Charlotte Ashman (10)	176

Windhill21 Primary School, Bishop's Stortford

Thomas Bilby (7)	177
Harrison Watts (7)	178
Mattia Rognoni (7)	180
Jaza	182
Sophie P	184
Scarlett Hobin-Smith (7)	185
Emily	186
Carmell Stirling (7)	188
Amelia Grey (7)	189
Alfie Howard (7)	190
Marley Nesemann-Webb (7)	191
Riley Edwards (7)	192
Farida	193
Freddie	194

THE POEMS

All About Me

When I'm older, I want to own a kids gym
I want to train them limb to limb
My favourite colour is sage-green
And I love all things aquamarine
My eyes are brown, the same as my hair
And my favourite animal is a panda bear
At kickboxing, I'm a red belt
In there, it's so hot, you want to melt
Upon my face, I wear glasses
I go to dancing, swimming and kickboxing classes
I use Spotify to work on my dance routine
And I have a treadmill, also known as a
running machine
I'm nine years old and my star sign is Cancer
My favourite of Santa's reindeer is Dancer
The school I go to is Audenshaw Primary
That it all there is to know about me.

Scarlett Rose Mcguire (9)
Audenshaw Primary School, Audenshaw

My Dog, Harper

My name is Robyn and I have a dog called Harper
She is like a Schnauzer mixed with a bit of whippet
She loves to play with her squeaky toy
Harper loves to bark at the postman
She loves to run off her lead on the field
Sometimes, but not all the time, we dress her
up in outfits
My mum says, "Stop messing with the dog, she's
not a baby!"
But I count her as a baby because she's always
looking for belly rubs
And also expects to be picked up like a baby every
single night
She loves to give kisses (licks)
She likes jumping over fences and being clumsy
and going on walks
She loves to chase cats and squirrels
She is not a big fan of baths
But loves her beef and cheese treats and all kinds
of food

For example; bacon, cheese, steak and any kind of beef or chicken
Me and my family love her very much.

Robyn Scarratt (9)
Audenshaw Primary School, Audenshaw

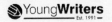

There's Only One Me

This is me, my name is Lucy
My mum also likes to call me Juicy
I have brown curly hair
At school, it even touches the back of my chair
I am the only one in my family with blue eyes
That look like bright blue skies
My favourite thing is to eat food
It just puts me in a great mood
I am very clumsy, I always fall
Sometimes I can't help it at all
There is one very special thing about me
On my cheek, I have a birthmark
Which I call my patch
There is nobody that will ever match.

Lucy May Walton (9)
Audenshaw Primary School, Audenshaw

My Life!

T hough I am not artistic, this was fun
H orses I love, I want to own one
I love to sing and dance
S o I practise every day

I 'm Katie or Kitty-Cat
S inger is my dream

M y friends call me The Leader
E ven though I dawdle a bit.

Katie Clowrey (9)
Audenshaw Primary School, Audenshaw

Me And My Beautiful Self

Today, I look to my beautiful self
And I love that I have mental health
I love my lovely face
I think my face has solved the case
Everyone says I look like beauty
I know myself as a fashion cutie
I admit I have a lovely face
I could even win in a race
I can even stay at the right pace
I love to draw and paint
When everybody sees it
They always seem amazed
I love to dress up and make stuff
I even like to bake pastry with crust.

Axia Reid-Vickers (8)
Beehive Preparatory School, Redbridge

My Favourite Person!

He is my friend, my best friend
He likes to eat pizza and eats ice cream
His name starts with 'S', just like me
He also smells like peach ice cream
When I hurt myself
My best friend comes to help me
He is nine years old
My best friend is a great footballer
He is a very naughty boy
Because he never makes me laugh
He has an Xbox
I have a PS4.

Samveer Dhani (8)
Beehive Preparatory School, Redbridge

All About Me!

All of the time, I read books
Look at my brand new hooks
Listen to what I exactly say
And I pick my sister up from school
Mostly every day
Bring me to the mall
Or I'll get lost like a ball
Under the bed, it's me!
That's how it's going to be
My sister is a bit pushy
Every time I go into the garden
The weeds get bushy!

Zachariah Qureshi (9)
Beehive Preparatory School, Redbridge

This Is Me!

I like sushi
But don't be pushy
My hair is brown
But I don't wear a crown
I have a cat
But he is not fat
I like the colour red
And I have a nice bed
I don't like elves
But I have a big shelf
I am high in intelligence
And I really like pie
And that is me!

Awais Mohammed Adam (8)
Beehive Preparatory School, Redbridge

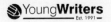
Me

J am is my favourite because it sounds like Jav
A mazing books make me happy a lot
V anilla is my favourite ice cream
E ating helps me when I'm hungry
R esting helps me when I'm tired
I like sleeping a lot
A nd having fun with my brother.

Javeria Chaudhry (8)
Beehive Preparatory School, Redbridge

Me

D awud likes tennis

A fter school, I eat some food

W hen I feel like it, I play some games

U p until Dad sends me to bed

D arwin is my school team that makes me red.

Dawud Shah (7)

Beehive Preparatory School, Redbridge

This Is Me!

When people think of me
They picture big brown eyes
Large rosy cheeks
And a smile you just couldn't miss!
But alas, such a cheerful person
Can't be cheerful all the time
For if you venture inside of me
It's not all kittens and rainbows...

Down in my feet is where my anger lies
Hot-headed, cries of fury
That's why I'm quite a foot-stomper

Upon my shoulders, it's a very dull area
It's where I like to be gloomy, sarcastic
And an 'eh, I'll do it later' person
So, don't be surprised if you see me slouch

From my wrists to my fingertips
Is the whimsical side of me
Teatime with the fairies
Swimming with the mermaids
It's the reason why my fingers wiggle

Oh, I can't forget that I'm a scaredy-cat in my
elbows
Headstrong and daring in my hips
A joker near my heart
They're all a part of me

The real me is deep inside myself though
Untouched, unseen, unknown
And yes, she's what makes me who I am
But come to think of it...
She's everything but me.

Shareen Islam
Bentinck Primary & Nursery School, Nottingham

All You See Is Outside Me

All you see is outside me
The cheerful, funny, sweet me
The rainbows all around me
A butter-won't-melt-in-my-mouth type me

But there is another me
A waiting-to-pounce me
An I-can't-be-bothered-to-do-that me
A helpless, bossy type of me

And inside there is another me
Full of mischievous ideas for pranks sort of me
A class clown sort of me.
And inside there is another me
Who is forever jealous, heartless with no life at all
An I never get anything me

And inside me is another me
Who is tiny and scared
The worrying, weird type of me
A superstitious me
And inside me is another me

Egotistic, responsible, trustworthy and helpful me
The 'she said not to touch that' type of me.

And deepest down, kept secretly
Is a black silhouette
The demon that hides inside of me

This is me.

Horia Noori
Bentinck Primary & Nursery School, Nottingham

This Is Me

The first thing you see is the outside me
The calm, smart, quiet whisper me
But the deeper you go, the more secrets you find
Some personal, some outside, and some
dangerous ones too

The other me, the give up, don't like this me
Bored all day, idle, loud
A butter-might-melt-in-my-mouth kind of me
But I still am calm and quiet too
Because that is just who I am

But there is another me
The scowling, hot-headed, very irritable me
Full of cheek and attitude
Lose my temper control kind of me
The might have jumped on my sister's back
When we were very young kind of me

And now, deepest down, mostly kept secret
A noisy, little child
The girl that hides inside of me.

Zoya Hussain
Bentinck Primary & Nursery School, Nottingham

This Is Me!

First, you'll need to put some ice into the bowl
Then sift some chilli powder on top
Now mix carefully
Wait five minutes for the ice to melt
So that it can blend the flavours together
After that, sprinkle some sprinkles
To balance the bitterness and create a bittersweet
aroma
Now pour in some coffee
And stir for approximately ten minutes
This will create a delicious soup textured mixture
Chop up some dark chocolate and heat it up
So that it can melt
This taste is worth more than a luxury
Now finally, pour this mixture into cupcake cases
And put it in the oven
And this would make me!

Eiliyah Ahad
Bentinck Primary & Nursery School, Nottingham

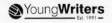

All You See Is Outside Me

All you see is outside me
My black long hair
The joyful smile on my face
My loneliness and braveness
And my sticky old breath
A trying hard type of me

But there's another me
A jealous, angry me
Emotional by small things me
A frustrated when he is angry me

And inside there's another me
Who's bored, lazy and who daydreams
An ignoring type of me
And inside there's another me
Selfish and wanting
A grass is always greener me

And deepest down
Kept secretly inside of me
A dream of becoming a footballer

This is me.

Hijran Zia
Bentinck Primary & Nursery School, Nottingham

Me

All you see is outside me
My printed smile and rose cheeks
The empty face with not a feature to see
The ice-cream-won't-melt-in-my-mouth type of me

But inside there's another me
The outside of school kind of me.
The do whatever I want type of me
And a cool and fun me
And inside there's another me
The cheeky type of me
And the joker of the family me

Inside there's another me
A frustrated kind of me
The I don't care type of me
The mad me
And lastly, very, very deep down
There's the lady in me.

Amalie-Rose Williams (10)

Bentinck Primary & Nursery School, Nottingham

This Is Me

All you see outside me is a big smile
A chatty, ratty person with a pen mark on the chin
A non-stop moving me

But inside there is another me
There is a girl that is always brave in hard times
And inside there is another me
Another me that is nervous
That little girl inside that pulls me to run away

And deeper there's another me
The jealous girl that wants more and more
The sky is blue more than me
And inside there is another me
The butter-wouldn't-melt-in-my-mouth me

But deeper there is another me
The calm angel me.

Aroua Serief (10)
Bentinck Primary & Nursery School, Nottingham

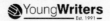

This Is Me!

All you see is outside me
The loving me
The kind and helpful me, happy me.
A never cracking egg me

But there's another me
The one who gets mad
Quitting if I lose
Throwing when I am sad me
A didn't do it blameless me

And inside there's another me
Crying when I go to sleep
Feeling like I am in a hopeless world
A wouldn't do anything me

And deepest down, kept secretly
The hopeless me
The one who thinks and looks
When did this happen? Who did it?

The boy that hides inside of me.

Haseeb Babar (10)
Bentinck Primary & Nursery School, Nottingham

All About Me

All you see is outside me
My cheerful smile, rosy cheeks
Confident, loyal, never sad
A butter-won't-melt-in-my-mouth type me

But inside there is another me
Lazy till playtime me
Fiddling with my books me
Not bothered to get up me
Never cleaning up type me

And inside there is another me
Smaller personality, very shy
Worried and scared
A boo will frighten me.

Aya Chebli
Bentinck Primary & Nursery School, Nottingham

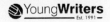

Who Is That?

He looks rather cheerful
Full of joy like vivid rainbows
I watch him laugh

He shouts an energetic cry
In the distance, the birds awake
But he has promises to keep
He's got to go to sleep

He falls asleep in his gentle bed
With thoughts of kittens in his head
Eating butter with lots of bread
Getting ready for the day ahead

This is me, Ali.

Ali Bashir
Bentinck Primary & Nursery School, Nottingham

This Is Me

Taking a moment, thinking
This is me originally
Taking a chance
Looking around
Slowly walking in the rain
Slowly taking in the rain
When my head was full of pain
Knowing that I am a natural person
Sometimes shy, but usually brave
Finding a rhythm
In the grass, beside the trees
Losing myself in the wonder of nature.

Ewa Petelska (11)
Bentinck Primary & Nursery School, Nottingham

Routine

A kennings poem

Pixelated creator
Ninja watcher
Number cracker
Roblox player
Computing producer
Joke master
Seven years listener
Non-fiction reader
Lego builder
Karate fighter
Piano creator
Minecraft gamer.

Muhammad Hashim Shahyan (7)
Bentinck Primary & Nursery School, Nottingham

This Is Me

S hopping is my favourite
O ther children I make friends with
H elping is the way jobs are done
A pples are my favourite fruit
N ice families are cuddly to me
A ngriness makes me sad.

Sohana Sheza (7)

Bentinck Primary & Nursery School, Nottingham

Maariya Mehmood

M y singing is beautiful
A rt is my hobby
A pples and pears are my favourite fruit
R aisins are my favourite
I am intelligent
Y ou are my best friend
A m I musical?

Maariya Mehmood (7)
Bentinck Primary & Nursery School, Nottingham

I Am Emmanuel

A kennings poem

Karate master
Xbox gamer
Pizza eater
Chocolate lover
Hockey player
Spicy food eater
Mess creator
Lego master
Goal scorer
Kind sharer
Milk drinker
Maths lover.

Emmanuel Mecha (7)

Bentinck Primary & Nursery School, Nottingham

This Is Me

Kovan
Kicking chairs
Wearing pears
Aiming high
Looking down
Reading poems
Reading books
But people think I'm a Russian doll
Doll after doll
Smiles and smiles
Stuck in smile wars
Until...
A tiny doll appears.

Kovan Salih Graham
Bentinck Primary & Nursery School, Nottingham

This Is Me

A pples and pears are not my favourite fruit
R eally like my sister Maryam
H omework is the best
A rt is my favourite subject
M y brothers help me a lot.

Arham Babar (7)
Bentinck Primary & Nursery School, Nottingham

Me

A kennings poem

Ballet dancer
Cupcake maker
Spicy food eater
Skater lover
Ice cream vanilla eater
Job lover
Swimmer splasher
Strawberry eater.

Eliza Yasin (7)
Bentinck Primary & Nursery School, Nottingham

Love Is All Around Me

I am full of kindness all around me
I am full of friendly people around me
I am full of love around me as I walk around nature

Nature talks to me as I walk down the woods
I am full of nature as I sprint in the woods
As I walk to the city, the birds call me for food

The city animals love me as I do my daily run
I'm full of positivity as nature sends its beautiful
animals to me
As I give the birds love, they give me love.

Maryam Nessa (9)
Bonner Primary School, Mile End

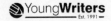
This Is Me

Caring, sharing and friendly
Sharing generosity
I like sewing and painting
Nothing extraordinary
Sometimes dramatic
Sometimes comical

I want to be the greatest doctor
One you have never seen
One who likes art
I want to pass all my hardest exams
I like to play Roblox with my best friend
I like to eat KFC

One shall never doubt me
Not even my cool teacher
I am as sharp as an eagle
And as swift as a bird
I soar in the sky
Nobody can stop me
I am unstoppable
I will fly as free as a dove

I am usually blissful
I can be charming
Watch out for me
You might see me soaring in the moonlit night
I am like a shooting star

Nobody can stop me
Nobody can
I will always try my best
Nobody can stand in my way
I never shatter into pieces of glass
Because of my inner strength

I am brave, strong and courageous
But most of all, I am not cowardly and fearful
I don't care about any challenges that I face
Because I am brave enough to face my fears
I care about being positive and enthusiastic
So turn your frowns upside down
A smile turns somebody's day into a mirthful day.

Aqsa Shahab (9)
Bonner Primary School, Mile End

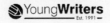
Lost In Thought

Feeling lost
Is a scary thing
It's when you have no one to turn to
When you feel sad
And you have no way of making yourself happy
It's when you've been double-crossed

You may be shivering
When you are lost
As if you are stuck
In a sheet of frost

You may feel lost
Maybe just when you're not feeling like you
When you feel you have no one to go to
When you feel sad and blue
When your head smokes like a barbecue
When you feel as wild as a buckaroo
Or when you feel like a robot who's missing a
certain screw

You may feel lost
When you are blinded with fury deep within you

When you are filled with the most blazing inferno
When you feel hollow in the head and cannot think
things through
Or just when you feel there is just nothing
you can do
That is when you are lost.

Qazi Tashfeen Ehsan (9)
Bonner Primary School, Mile End

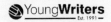

My Loud House

I live a pretty awesome life
I have my mother, father and two sisters
My house is a loud one

My little sister
Loves to scream
She also likes lots of cream!

My mother
She always cooks for us
It's always so loud, especially the kettle!

My father
Lounges in the bed
Watches his phone
And plays games!

My older sister
We don't get along
Only sometimes
But not for long...

And then there's me
I'm normally happy

I don't ask for much
I'm normally very quiet
But obviously, I do interact
With my very loud, loving family...

I love my family
And they love me back and I know it!

Jannah Hussain (9)
Bonner Primary School, Mile End

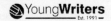

I Am Ikram

I am awesome
I am great
I am happy like a beautiful grape
Caring is me
Laughter is free
I like Pop Its
Why not pop one with me
I like chocolate, that's just me
I am Ikram
The greatest you'll ever see
I dream of a world of equality and peace.

Ikram Ali (9)
Bonner Primary School, Mile End

This Is Me

A kennings poem

Fortnite player
Chicken eater
Dream chaser
Piano taker
Arsenal hater
Ice cream craver
Cat lover
Man United supporter
This is me.

Muhammed Ayaan Islam (9)
Bonner Primary School, Mile End

All About Me!!

My grin beams from ear to ear
You will never see me shed a tear
I try to stay positive every day
Even when I'm feeling grey

I love rocking out on my bass guitar
The noise can travel extremely far
I also have a creative side
Which I definitely don't try to hide

I get on really well with all my friends
We'll all be close until the end
I love my family until the end of time
Even when my brother throws around slime

This is everything you need to know about me
And now I can clearly see
I am doing terribly well
Now I have finally come out of my shell!

Isabella Ava Cross (10)
Downsend School, Leatherhead

This Is Me

I love my family and friends
I have two dogs
And I don't like cats
I am a fiery red-head
A kind and funny person
I am a cousin
And a sister
And a daughter
I have always wanted a Yorkiepoo
I am terrible at art
But great at making my friends laugh
People always say
That they love the colour of my hair
When I go to the shops
I always ask if I can have a roll of sweets
Last but not least
I am a girl called Emma
This is me and I won't let anyone
Take my personality away from me.

Emma Clarke (10)
Downsend School, Leatherhead

This Is Me!

I'm funny, I'm kind
I'm quite annoying
You might find!

I'm shy at first
But when you get to know me
My craziness will burst!

I like to play FIFA
I'm a football diva
I play it for a club
But hate being a sub!

I'm obsessed with animals
I have two cats
That will lay on your lap
When you're having a nap!

I love my family
And have awesome friends
I do love sport
I normally get caught

When being cheeky
But I don't mind because...
This is me!

Emilia Davies (10)
Downsend School, Leatherhead

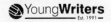

All About Me

This is me, happier than the sun
Always ready to have fun
Loves ice cream
And is sometimes
Caught up in a dream

This is me, baking all afternoon
Whilst singing a happy tune
Skating at Guildford spectrum
I have a lovely bedroom

I love my family lots and lots
I also like swirls and dots
I play the piano
I play the flute
I also have singing lessons too

All my friends, best friends
And best, best friends are super cool
And writing this poem, I know that I am too.

Jessica Ribet (10)
Downsend School, Leatherhead

If I Were...

If I were an animal
I would be a squirrel
I would wiggle my tail
And attract the males
I would climb on the tree
And enjoy what I could see

If I were a drink
I would be hot chocolate
I would bring people sweetness
As well as happiness

If I were a dog
I would be a Bichon Frise
I would run as much as I could
And give everyone a happy mood
I would make a cute pose all day long
And make everyone happy enough to sing a song.

Sheung Yu Ryanna Ng (10)
Downsend School, Leatherhead

The Splash!

I opened the door...
Splash! Splash! Splash!
Water running as my heart is racing
Up the stairs, I go
Dive in and do it again
My goggles fell off
I have no way to see
But my friend, called Tea, went to save me!
I fix my goggles on the way
But the lifeguard made me laugh
My goggles weren't fixed but...
Splash!
I fell in the water again and got back up
And then down the slide
That's how my swimming day went.

Jasmine Droutis (10)
Downsend School, Leatherhead

This Is Me

Waking up early is the worst
I think it might be a curse

I like baking cakes
When I eat too much, I start to ache

I love animals very much
Although they mostly run out of my clutch

I love my two dogs, they are the best
But sometimes they don't give me enough time to
rest

Most people say my sister is cute
But she is the opposite of mute

I love going to the sea
This is me.

Holly Dada (10)
Downsend School, Leatherhead

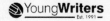

This Is Me

An inventive mind
I'm happy and kind
I have many skills
I wish I had gills

Coding is my all
Art makes me fall
I don't like school
Though sometimes it's a ball

Netball fan
I try to play when I can
It's just Mum, Dad and me
And no playful doggy

French is easy
But Spanish makes me queasy
I play the trumpet
But don't get me started on the cornet.

Harriet Hughes (10)
Downsend School, Leatherhead

This Is Me!

Happy, kind
A silly mind
Funny and weird
And always feared

Hockey hater
Talk to me later
Netball lover
And my annoying brother

Once my dog fell in a pond
I didn't use a magic wand
Fluffy and cute
But she's never on mute

I'm creative and arty
And I love a good party
It's just imaginative me
But I absolutely hate tea.

Lucy Guiney (10)
Downsend School, Leatherhead

51

Fat Cat

My cat is just a lump
When he gets off the couch
He makes a big thump
He's so wide
But he still walks around with pride
My cat lies around all day long
After he eats he will make a stinky pong
He is a lazy boy
Sometimes he sleeps
So you can mistake him for a toy
He is smelly
But you cannot compare that to his belly
My cat is fat.

Ryan Dekker (10)
Downsend School, Leatherhead

Dreams

In my dreams
I eat ice creams
I collaborate with Dream
My dreams turn into a shiny gleam
I have lots of dreams
A diet with all ice creams
Go to Dreamland for a tour
Gaming for three hours
Ramming others in the game...
Wait, is dreaming useless?
Not really

Energetic?
Yep
Useful?
Yeah
I want them to come true!

Ethan Chan (10)
Downsend School, Leatherhead

My Favourite Animal!

They roll around in mud
They need a bath in a tub
They are pink
Sometimes they look like they are covered in ink
They look cute when they are a piglet
And sometimes they might be a triplet
They like to eat plants
But they cannot dance
I think they are adorable
They are wonderful
What is this animal?

It is a pig.

Chloe Della (11)
Downsend School, Leatherhead

This Is Me

When I feel sad, I tell my mum
Thinking she wouldn't tell everyone
But then regret that
Because parents can't keep secrets
My dog can keep more secrets than them
Because dogs can only bark and whine
And humans do not know their language
But dogs can hear you
And every little thing you say...

Ria Kaur Sandhu (10)
Downsend School, Leatherhead

This Is Me

I live in water and on land
Never on sand
I love axolotls
Unlike plastic bottles
I'm a nature freak
But I'm real, real sleek
I've got animal facts
As tall as six Big Macs
I love Pokémon
Just like this song
What am I?

I am me.

Elliot Moore (10)
Downsend School, Leatherhead

My Favourite Animal

I have lots of prickles, sharp and spiky
I am very shy and only come out at night
I like to hide in dens and eat lots of food
I am very rare and mostly brown
I am hunted by lots of animals like owls
When I am scared, I curl up in a ball
What am I?

I am a hedgehog.

Marcus Young (10)
Downsend School, Leatherhead

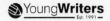
All About Me

When I feel sad
A game of cricket always helps
A big beautiful wildness walk helps
The smell of the woods always helps
Making Lego helps
Playing the drums and the guitar always helps
Running makes me feel better.

George Gale (10)
Downsend School, Leatherhead

This Is Me!

I'm the biggest cat in South Africa
I'm the fastest animal in the world
I'm a great hunter but I only pounce at night
No prey puts up a fight
What am I?

I'm an Acinonyx jubatus cheetah.

Tayla Smith (10)
Downsend School, Leatherhead

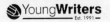

All About Me

I like kinetic sand
Because of how it feels in my hand
It makes me feel calm
When it rests in my palm

When it comes to football
I always keep in mind
I want to score goal after goal all the time.

Stanley Davenport (11)
Downsend School, Leatherhead

This Is Me

A kennings poem

I'm a...
Football keeper
Cricket player
Pokémon collector
Cat lover
Pizza eater
Xbox adorer
Nerf shooter
YouTube watcher
Scratch coder
And finally...
I'm Oscar.

Oscar Manly (10)
Downsend School, Leatherhead

I Care

I care,
I care about racism,
I care about climate change,
I care about my family and pets,
I care about my friends,
I care about my life,
And I care about the whole world.

Esme Rodulfo-Flatt (10)
Downsend School, Leatherhead

My Olympia

Hungry and lazy
But loveable all the same
I look at her
As she wanders around
In her metal cage
Eating weeds
To help plants grow
This is my tortoise, Hello.

George Dale (10)
Downsend School, Leatherhead

This Is Me

A kennings poem

I am a...
Hockey player
Movie watcher
Waffle maker
Small girl
Cool girl
Deep sleeper
Food eater
Dog lover
Chip eater
COVID hater.

Amelie Chellun (10)
Downsend School, Leatherhead

What I Care About

I care about football
I care about food and drinks
I care about my life
I care about climate change
But what I don't care about is money.

Billy Maylin (10)
Downsend School, Leatherhead

This Is Me

Rising star
Amazing finisher
Funny boy
Fantastic defender
Yelling on the wing

This is me...

Raffy Fewings (10)
Downsend School, Leatherhead

This Is Me

A haiku

I like my doggy
I like eating chocolate cake
I like takeaway.

Sam Russell (10)

Downsend School, Leatherhead

Me And My Metal Detector

M e and my detector have got a good signal.
E ffort trying to find a good coin.
T hen I find out that it's a good silver coin.
A t last, I found something good.
"L unch break!" my papa shouted. Ham sandwich, yum.

"D avid, back to detecting!" said Papa.
E xciting, detecting for a good find.
T hen when I said that, I start to hear *beebbb!*
E xcitedly digging a hole. Papa said, "Remember to fill in your hole!"
"C oin!" shouted Papa.
T he coin seemed to be copper.
I n the afternoon, about to go home.
N ow taking my boots off.
G etting in the car, getting ready to go home.

David Mason (9)
Langcraigs Primary School, Glenburn

Me

E than is addicted to football
T raining every day to get better
H aving a lot of fun playing with friends
A lways dreaming I'll be professional
N on-stop playing, having a good time

M issing shots is the worst
C aring when someone gets injured
C elebrating when I score
A fter scoring, I'm really happy
F inishing goals is amazing
F alling or diving like Raheem Sterling is stupid
E arly goals are great
R acism to players is terrible
T hree goals is a hat-trick
Y es, sir, I can boogie is a great Scotland song.

Ethan McCafferty (10)
Langcraigs Primary School, Glenburn

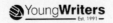
The All About Me Rap

I like football,
I'm a magic midfielder.
Just like my cat, my boots are black.
I like gaming, FIFA 22,
I've been bossing the new game out.
And I've been rocking on my guitar,
Went to practice last night.
Now I sound like a god with a plectrum.
Swimming, let's talk about swimming,
I don't even go swimming.
Because I passed my test,
And now I can swim around the bend.
Now, let's finish off this rap,
And talk about my growth.
My grandparents say that I'm really tall,
But somehow, I'm not even the tallest in the class.

Charlie McLaren (9)
Langcraigs Primary School, Glenburn

The Football Gamer Rap!

I like football, maybe not you.
I say achoo, get a tissue.
Maybe some gaming, FIFA 22?
I was back in the garden playing FIFA 51.
I love it and you should too.
When I was playing football, the crossbar challenge.
I got it on the first try and you should too.
When I was playing Minecraft yesterday,
I beat the Ender Dragon and said, "Hooray!"
My mum tells me I game too much,
But I said, "No, not a touch."

Daniel McGregor (8)
Langcraigs Primary School, Glenburn

Wonderful

W here I live, it is nice weather.

O ne day, it was very warm outside.

N o one was expecting this warm weather.

D o you know that it was twenty-nine degrees last summer?

E nd of the day, it is still quite warm.

R ound my bit, it gets quite warm in the summer.

F or the summer, my family buys ice lollies.

U nfun it was because it was warm, so I just

L ooked out the window.

Lucy Robertson (9)
Langcraigs Primary School, Glenburn

Me

H elpful person,
A wesome at netball.
N ice, movie lover,
N ot always in for a fight.
A mazing at life,
H obbies are my favourite thing!

S port is my best thing.
C anada is the place I want to go.
O xford is the place I want to go for college.
T ill I stop living, I will fight
T ip for life, just have fun!

Hannah Scott (10)
Langcraigs Primary School, Glenburn

This Is Me

T he girl who is a good singer,
H elpful all the time.
I love to listen to music,
S inging is my favourite hobby and people think I'm good at it.

I passed my grade two singing exams last year.
S ad is never how I feel.

M y friends are all kind and awesome,
E very member of my family is wonderful.

Orlay McEnhill (9)
Langcraigs Primary School, Glenburn

This Is Me

T he girl who gets called small,
H elpful, but only if I feel like it.
I got asked if I could be someone's football!
S ometimes I like to sing with Orlay.

I like to listen to music.
S ometimes I am sad, but hardly ever.

M y dog is so cute.
E lephants are one of my favourite animals.

Ellis Adams (8)
Langcraigs Primary School, Glenburn

I Am...

I am happy and kind,
I wish for every adult to have a job.

I am clever and adventurous,
I worry that a lot of people
Are not getting a good education.

I am optimistic and energetic,
I hope that we can fix
All the problems in the world!

I am messy and chilled,
I pretend that there are
No problems in the world.

Ellie Jane Longwill (10)
Langcraigs Primary School, Glenburn

My Name

L ollipops are my favourite sweets.

A pple and chocolate are good.

U nique, being the only one of its kind.

R esin, substance produced by some trees.

E arthenware of baked clay.

N ightdress, loose dress that women or girls wear to sleep in.

Lauren Thomson (9)

Langcraigs Primary School, Glenburn

What Makes Me!

H elpful, kind and true.
E very day, a different day.
A rty in so many ways.
T o be sad, very little shows.
H air blonde as you can see.
E arth, I care about very much.
R ainbow feelings, but mostly positive.

Heather Nicholson (8)

Langcraigs Primary School, Glenburn

Me!

E xcellent at horse riding, I'm speedy and fast
L ovely to others, I make people laugh
L azy, when I'm in the house
I 'm a super story writer with great imagination
S mart in school, working hard and doing well.

Ellis Duffin (10)
Langcraigs Primary School, Glenburn

The Worry

I am worried and anxious,
I am worried if COVID will last forever!
I hope pollution will end and nothing will be hurt.
I wish world problems will be solved,
I dream that the world would be safe and clean,
I worry about the world's future.

Aimee Dunn (10)
Langcraigs Primary School, Glenburn

All About Me

T iny in size,
H appy all the time.
I maginative,
S assy.

I like to play football.
S our sweets are my favourite.

M y name is Reid.
E very time I run, I fall.

Reid Hughes (9)
Langcraigs Primary School, Glenburn

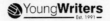
Poppy The Hamster

P etrified all the time.

O verworked all the time.

P atient to get food all the time.

P ounces all the time when Poppy hamster gets food.

Y awns, and you see Poppy's yellow teeth all the time.

Riley Higginson (9)

Langcraigs Primary School, Glenburn

Me

A lways confident, brave and caring
R eally energetic with friends the same
W onderful, bright and happy personality
E very day is a Minecraft day
N ever doubt myself, no matter what.

Arwen Bowskill (10)

Lungcraigs Primary School, Glenburn

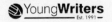

Ronnie's Marvellous Poem

I am sporty and small
I wish to be a footballer
I am good at drawing and I like doing it
I wonder if COVID can be fully cured
I feel excited when I play football
I hear the Hampden roar.

Ronnie Millar (10)
Langcraigs Primary School, Glenburn

Marvellous Me

R andom drawer with brilliant ideas
O dd eater and very picky
M ysterious big writer
Y oung and a big family.

Romy Easdon (10)
Langcraigs Primary School, Glenburn

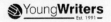

My Future

I want to be a lawyer
They look cool
And it seems like they rule
About you, I have no clue
I'm imaginative
Your situation is in my hands
Honestly, I'll take care of it with class
Let me graduate first, then I'll see
No one knows in twenty years where I'll be
If I become a lawyer I'll be the best you've ever had
I'll be so good, people will want to copy and paste
I don't know what law I'll be in
There's criminal law, law of tort, law and morality
Law of justice, judicial creativity
And balancing conflicting interests
I'm imaginative and creative
And will solve your problems in five seconds
I'll think of you as an innocent client
Surely you'll win, even if my pieces of paper
are thin

I'm determined, so if I lose, I'll try again
I'm studying a law book
Soon, I'll conquer and people will only give me good looks.

Gifty Ezirike (11)
Seaview Primary School, Belfast

All About Me!

My name is Anna and I like to eat bananas
I have a cute, cuddly cat called Loki
When he jumps up on my bed, I say, "Are
you joking?"
When I'm in school, I'm as busy as a bee
But when my teacher gives me more, I'm like, "Are
you kidding me?"
I'm really sporty and play football
What makes it even better is that I'm as fast as a
lightning bolt
I like to clean and once I'm finished cleaning
I like to go and do a bit of reading
I'm quite good at drawing and like to organise
If I was not organised, then I would die
I am friendly and adventurous
But if there's something I don't know about, then I
am curious.

Anna McComb
Seaview Primary School, Belfast

This Is Me

This is me
I play football as fast as lightning
I am really competitive and sporty
Boxing is fun and I love it, I dream of becoming
world champion!
I love to watch movies with my granda
and granny in my spare time, and play the PS5
I have a little brother named Cooper, he's just the
best.
I have brown hair and blue shiny eyes.
When I grow up
I want to be a professional footballer
I want to play for Chelsea, that would
be my dream
My age is eleven
My brother's age is four
I really enjoy making food at my granny's house
every Friday, we have lots of fun.

Carter Whyte (11)

Seaview Primary School, Belfast

I Could Be...

If I were a leaf
I could stick to my tall tree
And breathe the fresh breeze
But I could fly far away
Through the storm
And over the sea
Or somewhere I don't even want to be
Oh, this is not me
What could I be?

I could be a bee
With a hive on a tree
A hive out of gold
Where I'll never be cold

But wait, there's a problem
I can't communicate with them
Oh, I don't want that
I don't need a tree to stick to

I don't need to be a bee
How silly
It's best to be me.

Hsuan-Jui Chang (11)

Seaview Primary School, Belfast

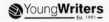

CD's Poem

My name is Corey-Dede
My nickname is CD
And this is a poem all about me
I love fast food
Like McDonald's, KFC, Burger King
I can't stop thinking which is best
I need a break and need to rest
All the girls think games are lame
Even though they're missing out
It makes me angry and want to shout
I think I'm pretty funny
Because I pretend to be a dummy
Sometimes I am silly
And I'm very chilli
Every time I'm happy
I'm very flappy
This poem is gonna end
Bye, my little friend.

Corey-Dede Kirkland (10)
Seaview Primary School, Belfast

This Is Me

I love my dog
She is called Kara
I'm not going to lie
I love animals
Especially dogs
I treat Kara every day
With love and respect
She is my whole life
I can't live without her

She has a boyfriend called Ace
He's my cousin's dog
He has a big face
He is very chubby
They lie together and cuddle

It is so cute when she is sleeping
But when she's awake, she's a demon
She eats my feet and my fingers
She is amazing, she is mine
This is me.

Faith Mcalorum (10)
Seaview Primary School, Belfast

All About Me

P olite and kind at all times
H ungry every second of the day
O ranges are my favourite fruit
E lephants are my most liked animal
N othing goes past me when I'm in goal
I am a very adventurous boy
X ylophone is my favourite instrument

B old in frightening events
L ove my family
A wesome at FIFA
Y ellow is my favourite colour
N ike is my favourite brand
E ntertaining every day
Y oung, tall, smart.

Phoenix Blayney (10)
Seaview Primary School, Belfast

What I'm Like

I am lazy in the morning
But wide awake at night
In the darkness, I must admit
I'm like an owl with my sight
I play my drums loud and clear
But my friend says I hurt her ears
I would play with my cat all day
Give her a treat when I get home from school
If I had a bad day
She would make me cool
My eyes are like a misty storm
And my hair is like a golden sword
I'm as tall as a giraffe
So when people say, "Oh, you're so tall"
All I do is laugh.
This is me!

Lilith Maguire (11)
Seaview Primary School, Belfast

Me In Haikus

Haiku poetry

I am...
I am sarcastic
I am queen of Nintendo
I am good at maths

I like...
I like good music
I like to learn Japanese
I like anime

I have...
I have good talent
I have got a good guitar
I have a sister

I have been...
I have been to Wales
I have been to Liverpool
I have topped Cavehill

I want to...
I want to draw good
I want to go to Japan
I want to be safe.

Esmee Manton (10)

Seaview Primary School, Belfast

This Is Boye Li!

This is me, people call me smart
I like drawing or painting art
I like playing, especially gaming
I love reading
And I really hate singing
I have two goldfish
But their food is very peckish
I have a very annoying little brother
That is not like any other
My mum and dad drive a car
That's faster than a shooting star
And there's COVID-19...
It's absolutely horrible
And makes everybody sob
This is me!

Boye Li (11)
Seaview Primary School, Belfast

Lexi's Lovely Poem

I'm like a lightning bolt
When I wear football shoes
I'm very curious, which can lead to something new
I love food, I think it's really tasty
I think I'm fun and a little bit crazy
Halloween is my favourite, I love dressing creepy
But at the end of that night, I tend to get really sleepy
I'm an animal lover, especially my dog
My favourites are turtles
I also like frogs
This is me.

Lexi Harker Quin (11)
Seaview Primary School, Belfast

This Is Me

I describe myself as smart and sporty
I watch TV shows such as Rick and Morty
I'm like a cheetah on a football pitch
When it comes to knowledge, I'm very rich
If I'm mad I play games to be happy
When I play football, all of my touches are zappy
I am tired at the end of the day
And little me just can't play
I always try to be as funny as can be
Smart, fun and sporty and that's just me.

Jake McKinley (10)
Seaview Primary School, Belfast

My Life In A Nutshell

I love bees
You might find a beehive on trees
I find some things hideous
You might think of me as very tedious

I'm a fast walker
A slow talker
I'm not very funny
I don't like stories

I don't like bats
But I do like cats
Spiders? Yikes
I hate them creepy-crawly scary spiders
Patterns are confusing
My favourite planet is Saturn.

Abir Khan
Seaview Primary School, Belfast

My Most Amazing Achievement!

I am a...
Daydreamer
Cake eater
Friend maker
A sketcher
A rower
And a gamer
A collector
Bird watcher
Brother annoyer
Toy cuddler
And a crafter
Also a drawer
Spider hater
Cat lover
A walker
Slow typer
But a fast talker

These are all my achievements
And don't forget
This is me!

Mikolaj
Seaview Primary School, Belfast

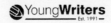

Caleb

I'm as silly as a squirrel
Adventurous as a rat
Lonely like a wolf
Sweet as cake
As kind as a peach
And as flashing fast as a lion
I'm as quiet as a koala
I'm as lazy as Garfield on a Monday
As hyper as a puppy
Worried like a robber on Wednesday
My favourite colour is green like grass
I'm as invisible as a chameleon.

Caleb Smyth (10)
Seaview Primary School, Belfast

This Is Me!

I crochet a lot with a ball of wool
When I finish, I see a hole
The colours I use are white and yellow
Just like my favourite colours of my fellow
I love my food, it is very good
Sometimes I'm lonely
But it's lovely when I'm not
I'm very organised and I'm as busy as a bee
I love peaches and beaches
And this is me!

Maja Skwiercz (10)
Seaview Primary School, Belfast

This Is Me

Football player
Chocolate eater
Sweetie lover
Kick-boxer
Family lover
Friends lover
Little Mix lover
Coke drinker
Girl adventurer
Sporty human
Dressy girl
Football fan
Book reader
Very creative
Drawing lover
Very active
Artist
Always watching the clock
Tick-Tock!
This is me.

Saskia McLaughlin
Seaview Primary School, Belfast

My Track Star Rabbit!

My track star rabbit
She's as fast as lightning speed
She goes through a hole in the garden
House to house, garden to garden
At night, she's a super spy
In the daytime, as cute as can be
We pet her, we feed her
She follows wherever we go
But nobody seems to know
She's a track star rabbit at night
This is me!

Twinkle Chen (11)
Seaview Primary School, Belfast

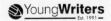

Harry Mckee

I'm a Fanta-holic
I love it so much
Venom is the best villain
In my opinion
I love to draw
Aliens are interesting
It's fun to learn about them
Reading books is fun to do
I'm good on the court with basketball
But sometimes I fall and cut my knee
My Kryptonite is the cold, it's very bold
This is me!

Harry McKee (11)
Seaview Primary School, Belfast

My Life

L ove for family
E nergetic person
W onderful, I help people
I mpressive to family
S mart, helps out

M agnificent hair
A mazing at football
C at lover
K angaroo, I like kangaroos
L ewis is my name
E lephant's like me when I stomp.

Lewis Mackle (11)
Seaview Primary School, Belfast

The Dragos Poem

D eadly, friendly, like a lion
R eally happy all the time like a dog on a walk
A n animal lover, I can't lie
G oing as fast as the Flash in basketball, that's what I love to do
O verreactor like in a movie
S mart as an ant, I love maths and that's what makes me, me.

Dragos Petras (11)
Seaview Primary School, Belfast

This Is Me!

I am an animal lover, but I can't lie
Coby the dog is my favourite
If I look into the light
The sun shines so bright
It blinds me in the eyes
My family gives me a spark
That makes my heart glow
My family and dog keep me alive
If I didn't have them, I would be in a fright.

Yazmin Akay (11)
Seaview Primary School, Belfast

Aaron's Favourite Things

Blue eyes remind me of the sky
And green eyes remind me of a plain green field
Green eyes remind me of vegetables
I love peas and broccoli
Seeing forests in autumn is like seeing my
favourite food
Which is chicken dinner, because of the colours of
the leaves.

Aaron McMullan
Seaview Primary School, Belfast

This Is Me

I am...
As sweet as sugar
As small as an ant
A heart of gold
Super at hockey
Sister annoyer
As cold as ice
As silly as a cat
As busy as a bee
A nature lover
As excited as a dog getting treats
This is me!

Olivia Doherty (10)
Seaview Primary School, Belfast

Amelia's Amazing Poem!

I am a...
Track runner
A lot of fun
Great reader
Bad leader
All nighter
Really bad fighter
Quite funny
Love bunnies
Food lover
Love my bedcovers
Really lazy
Always crazy
This is me.

Amelia Gogacz (10)
Seaview Primary School, Belfast

How To Create Me!

To create me, you will need:
A lot of fun
A tint of food-lover
A dash of movie lover
A pound of good friends
A splash of loving to party
A small amount of fashion
A teaspoon of dark, blonde hair
A bowl of hazel eyes
And a dip from KFC for dinner

Now you need to:
Add some sport to keep healthy
Add a mix of three teaspoons of fun and mischief
Then add some chocolate to sweeten stuff up
Then stir for five minutes and wait half an hour
Add some melted ice cream, non-melted will ruin it
Then put it in the oven for two hours

Then you have me! Hello! Nice to meet you!

Sian Bevan (10)
St Thomas Cantilupe CE Primary, Hereford

This Is Me

A is for afternoon snacks
B is for bedtime reading
C is for crafty crosswords
D is for Dr Who
E is for everyday obstacles
F is for fun and games
G is for good things
H is for happy days
I is for I don't know what to put
J is for jokes and clowns
K is for karate chop
L is for learning fast
M is for morning hair
N is for never naughty
O is for open the chocolate box
P is for Phoebe, my name
Q is for Queen's Jubilee
R is for roly-poly
S is for sassy sister, Tilly
T is for Tilly, the terror is coming
U is for utterly ridiculous

V is for very funny. Not!

W is for Wednesday dinner

X is for X-rays that hopefully will never come

Y is for you know me yet?

Z is for zip it, this poem is about me.

Phoebe Parry (10)

St Thomas Cantilupe CE Primary, Hereford

This Is Me

Sarcastic, kind
A not so fast mind
Maths is my superpower
But English makes me cower

A swipe, I paint
I am an amazing artistic kid
A life-long art fan
I paint whenever I can

I'm sweet, I'm sour
Depending on the hour
Sometimes I make a riot
Sometimes I crave the quiet

Most days are good days
And then I'll make you laugh
But some days are bad days
And I'm sad, but just for a while

So this is me
Sometimes sad, mostly happy
And to bring sad moods to a super-quick end
I rely on my crazy gang of lunatic friends.

Natasha Ingram (10)
St Thomas Cantilupe CE Primary, Hereford

How To Make Me..

To create me, you will need:
A cosy warm bedroom with a TV and a bunk bed
Old packets of food lying around
Two tablespoons of weirdness and creativity
A pinch of meanness
One tablespoon of fun
A dash of angriness
And lastly, one tablespoon of confidence

To finish it off, you will need to:
Mix it all up
Add in the happiness
Put a drop of vanilla in
Stir it all together
Put it in the oven for thirty minutes
And wait till it's bubbly
Then, add my favourite sweets to top it all off

This is me!

Rhian Oldaker (10)
St Thomas Cantilupe CE Primary, Hereford

This Is Me

To create me, you will need:
A love for art
A love for baking
A collection of Horrible Histories books
A cute dog
Conkers in every corner
A Harry Potter wall

Method:
Add 11lb of art
Mix in a Harry Potter filled room
Stir gently whilst adding a love for baking
Next, add a pinch of dislike for spiders
Spread along a tray with parchment paper
Make sure your dog doesn't eat it
Sprinkle on a cup of clumsiness and Horrible
Histories books
Leave to bake at 130°C for twenty minutes.

Mila Tomev (10)
St Thomas Cantilupe CE Primary, Hereford

To Create Me

To create me, you will need:
A PS4 in a box and a TV
A pack of Uno cards
A chocolate bar - half-eaten
A piece of wallpaper
1,000 Robux on Roblox on a phone
An X-shot ready to shoot someone

Now you need to:
Add the PS4 and the TV in a bowl
Mix in a half-eaten chocolate bar
Push in a phone with 1,000 Robux on Roblox
Stir roughly while adding a piece of wallpaper
Drop in an X-shot ready to shoot someone
Then cook for ten minutes
Sprinkle the Uno cards on top
Now you have me!

Ashton Brown (10)
St Thomas Cantilupe CE Primary, Hereford

My Favourite Animal

It has two flippers,
It lives on land and has wings,
But is unable to fly,
It slides down and up hills,
It swims well but waddles on land,
It's black and white,
But when it is a baby
It is grey, white and black,
It lives in the Antarctic
And dives in the water to eat fish,
It catches fish with its beak,
And runs from danger
What is it?

Flynn Beard (11)
St Thomas Cantilupe CE Primary, Hereford

Adeoluwa

A n author is what I want to be
D ear to me are my loved ones
E verlasting is my happiness
O ceans of intelligence and waves of peace
L ove is my centre, it is who I am
U nique, strong and brave
W arm, kind, passionate and helpful
A mazing and ingenious, I am me.

Adeoluwa Amos (8)
St Thomas Cantilupe CE Primary, Hereford

Bubbly Bruno

B ucket of kindness and helpfulness
R espectfulness
U seful for playing games
N oisy laughs
O ccasionally naughty

A universe of games
A tub of maths
A mind full of laughs
A sprinkle of naughtiness
A box of books
A sprinkle of madness.

Bruno Janusz (8)
St Thomas Cantilupe CE Primary, Hereford

Buzzy Bella

A ton of smiles
An ocean of kindness
A ton of mess and happiness
A pinch of cheekiness
A tin of love and cuddles
A pan of kisses
A pinch of sassiness
A love of a beautiful smile
A pinch of intelligence
A flick of naughtiness
A lorryload of love.

Bella Hall (8)
St Thomas Cantilupe CE Primary, Hereford

Magical Olivia

O ccasionally likes sleeping and good at being lazy

L ovely at making people laugh

I ntelligent as a queen

V ery kind and sweet

I ndoors lover and loves drawing

A ngel of being quiet in school.

Olivia Racis (8)
St Thomas Cantilupe CE Primary, Hereford

My Favourite Animal

A creature of land, not sea or sky
It has big ears and four feet
And it is not extinct
It lives in two countries
And it has two different species
It is large, not small
What is it called?

It is an elephant.

Liam Jones (10)
St Thomas Cantilupe CE Primary, Hereford

Lovely Lola

L ovely and happy
O nly has a touch of fanciness
L ots of anger
A bottle of plant lover

J ewellery lover
A mazing at singing
N ame is Lola
E scalator lover.

Lola Jane Carlson (8)
St Thomas Cantilupe CE Primary, Hereford

Lovely Olivia

A drop of sassiness
A ton of love
A pinch of smile
A handful of smart
A ton of school
A pinch of magic
A ton of robots
A drop of pollen
A handful of recorders
A pinch of shell
A ton of deep sea.

Olivia Underhill (9)
St Thomas Cantilupe CE Primary, Hereford

Joyful Jaya

A pinch of joy
An ocean of kindness
A world of creativity
An ounce of insane
A drop of inspiration
A sprinkle of talent
A ton of messy room
A universe of power
A tunnel of laziness
A city of talking.

Jaya Shellam (9)
St Thomas Cantilupe CE Primary, Hereford

Athletic Alan

A handful of joy
A bottle of loud
A world of athletic ability
A universe of jokes
A land of football tricks
A pinch of cheekiness
A handful of talent
A sprinkle of annoyance
A universe of goalkeeping.

Alan Podgorski (8)
St Thomas Cantilupe CE Primary, Hereford

Champion Cobie

C heeky and tries to get away with it
O bvious of trying to sleep in the morning
B est at doing spelling
I nviting in taking friends home
E ngine of talking about all my memories.

Cobie Jackson (8)

St Thomas Cantilupe CE Primary, Hereford

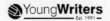

Fabulous Fabian

F air and square
A bsurd, amazing and protective
B etween good and evil
I mperfect like everyone else
A bounds with happiness
N ormally enjoys playing games.

Fabian Rucki (9)
St Thomas Cantilupe CE Primary, Hereford

Magic Maria

M essy, happy and I love food
A ctive, funny and I love dolls
R ed is my favourite colour
I ncredible at tennis and swimming
A mazing at looking after animals.

Maria Tomev (8)
St Thomas Cantilupe CE Primary, Hereford

Amazing Alarna

A ttention needed a lot
L oving person
A nnoying sister to my brother
R efreshingly kind
N ervous around strangers
A mazing girl.

Alarna Lloyd (8)
St Thomas Cantilupe CE Primary, Hereford

Magical Arshya

A ngel at being nice
R efreshingly kind
S uper at drawing
H appy when singing
Y oung and intelligent
A mazing at dancing.

Arshya Sanju (8)
St Thomas Cantilupe CE Primary, Hereford

Oliver

A pinch of rice
A bucket of naughtiness
A drop of sleepiness
A spoon of wildness
A handful of craziness
A ton of speed
An ocean of adventures.

Oliver Zheng (8)
St Thomas Cantilupe CE Primary, Hereford

Jazzy Julia

J azzy with brightness
U niverse of sassiness
L avender scents
I ncludes people in games
A ccident of mistakes.

Julia Koleczek (9)
St Thomas Cantilupe CE Primary, Hereford

Joyful Gina

A handful of kindness
A bottle of beauty
A drop of helpfulness
A bucket of creativity
A ton of quiet
An ocean of shyness.

Gina Tangiaritsakul (8)

St Thomas Cantilupe CE Primary, Hereford

Magical Mariana

M essy

A rtist

R efreshing

I ntelligent

A musing

N ormal

A mazing.

Mariana Campos (8)

St Thomas Cantilupe CE Primary, Hereford

Eager Eint

E very day, I do lots of crafts
I ncredible at art
N ice to everyone
T ricks people.

Eint Myat (8)
St Thomas Cantilupe CE Primary, Hereford

Terrific Ted

T errific at being lazy
E xcellent at stroking dogs
D evious at eating biscuits.

Ted Waters (8)

St Thomas Cantilupe CE Primary, Hereford

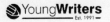
Respectful Rio

R arely mean, always respectful
I ncredible at football
O bviously funny.

Rio Whittingham (9)
St Thomas Cantilupe CE Primary, Hereford

This Is Me

A dash of grated crazy cheese
A loud lime
A jar of happiness honey
A jug of my wacky friends
A roll of smart sushi
15g of mad mangoes
A tub of positive passionfruit
A sprinkle of sweet sugars
1tbsp of laughing lemonade

First, add in the dash of grated crazy cheese
Then, add one loud lime
Next, pour in the jar of happiness honey
Add in a jar of my wacky friends
Mix in smart sushi rolls
Add 15g of mad mangoes
Sprinkle the smart sugars into the laughter
lemonade
And drizzle it over the positive passionfruit
Add that to the rest of the mixture.

Beth Williams (11)
West Ashton Primary School, West Ashton

This Is Me!

I can be rude but kind
I have a super speedy mind
I am known as clever and confident
Maths makes my brain speed
But English slows my brain down

I am a crazy dog lover
My favourite is my dog, Hunni
I am an elephant admirer
My life would be crushed
If the world was created without animals
As well as the ones in the sea
All animals are for me

I am a vegetarian
A no-meat eater
Saving animals is the thing for me
I enjoy eating healthily
It's a new goal for me
But I love to have a treat once in a while
Crisps or chocolate, no sweets for me

I am a drawing master
It's another hobby
I'm an acro dancer in training
I am very passionate about dance
I also have fun with singing, no matter the tune

I have pinky red lips
Sometimes a bit dry
I have very curly dark brown hair
Just like a large, brown, round mop
My eyes are usually green grapes
They can be a bit blue or sometimes even browny

I love my family and friends
My family gives me warmth and shelter
My friends give me entertainment as well as my
family
My family also gives me food on my plate and
water in my cup
They give me a bed to sleep on,
Even though I don't like sleeping much
Thanks to them, my life is great
They both give me love and support

I am usually the one to start a chat
But I also crave the quiet so I have space to calm down
I am extremely grateful for my clubs too
I am thankful for everything I have

So now you know this is me!

Deni Donovan (11)
West Ashton Primary School, West Ashton

This Is Me

I'm a light sleeper
But a healthy eater

I'm very funny
And like honey

I'm a footballer
And a good helper

I have a messy bedroom
And I can't presume

I'm a sports lover
With an annoying brother

I love dogs
But scared of hogs

I don't like cats
Neither rats

I have a house
But not a mouse

And this is what makes me, me!

Abigail Squires (10)
West Ashton Primary School, West Ashton

This Is Me!

A marshmallow sheet
Cup of sparkles
A jar of happiness
Spoonful of school
A pinch of craziness
Cup of sprinkles
A jar of laughter
Half a cup of enthusiasm
A teaspoon of ripe strawberries
Pinch of glitter
A jug of colour

First, pour a cup of laughter into a bowl of
warm milk
Then, stir with a sprinkle spoon, add half a cup
of enthusiasm
Pour a pink jug of colour into a blue buttered tray
Carefully add a teaspoon of ripe strawberries and
a spoonful of school
Slowly, pour a cup of sparkly boba bubbles into the
mix

Next, get a pinch of glitter and another pinch
of craziness
Stir up the mix and quickly pour it into the glitter-
covered tray
Let it bake for 15 mins, then let it cool down for
another 15 mins
Finally, get a marshmallow sheet and cut it
into quarters
Place the marshmallow sheet onto a plate and
place the cake on it
Then eat!

Isabel Hinds (9)
West Ashton Primary School, West Ashton

This Is Me

There's a lion of bravery in me
Roaring and leaping proudly
But if I come across my greatest fear
It will curl up in the shadows

There's a kitten of curiosity in me
Always lurking around
And if I find something I don't know of
It will make me go back to school

There's a dog of fun in me
Jumping and having a blast
And even if I'm in a maths test
It will fight back at long division

There's a mouse of stress in me
A common enemy
But if it lets me down again
No cheese for dinner

There's a tiger of self-confidence in me
One of my best friends
But if you want to see it at its worst
You'll ask me to read this out!

Melody Turner (9)
West Ashton Primary School, West Ashton

This Is Me!

I am a dancer
And a very graceful prancer
I am the bookworm of the century
And I know how to write an entry
I am a school-lover
Who has an annoying brother
Easily discouraged is me
And that's who I am meant to be
Correction isn't my strong point
Because it usually disappoints
I forget everything new
But remember everything old about me and you
I am a maths whizz
Who is always ready to take on a quiz
I am as slow as a snail
But I am always the first to grab the mail
I am annoying when intended
As I am not well comprehended
I am cold but bold
I am a light sleeper

And an animal keeper
I am also as clumsy as Humpty-Dumpty!
This is me!

Keilani McOwan (10)

West Ashton Primary School, West Ashton

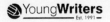

This Is Me

Kind and caring
With the radio blaring
My favourite subject is English
Even though I never finish

Dancing like a ballerina
And having cousins in Argentina
Pizza is the best thing that happened to me
Don't judge me, just let me be

I have long, brown hair
And I love going to the funfair
I have done gym since I was two years old
And when I go to Co-op
Ben & Jerry's is always sold

I love walking my dog
And I love doing all sorts of jobs
Salted Caramel ice cream is the best thing on
Earth
I have also loved carbonara since birth

My zodiac sign is Leo
And my puppy is called Rio
I am good at swimming
And I also love sprinting!

Coco Jones (10)

West Ashton Primary School, West Ashton

This Is Me

On Mondays, my gran picks me up
I can see Willow and Midnight, the kittens
Dinner there till six o'clock
Then my gran takes me home for a bath

Playing with my friends all break
Time to go in, then we all learn
After working, it is time for lunch
We are in bubbles so no hugging my BFF
Time to learn again till three o'clock

On Tuesdays, it is PE
So we need PE uniform
After French, we do PE till home time.

Rose Stower-Draper (10)
West Ashton Primary School, West Ashton

This Is Me

T alking is nice, I like doing it sometimes, I'm sometimes quiet, depends where I am
H air as dark as black
I wear purple glasses all day, every day
S ometimes I'm active, sometimes I'm not

I love playing with my friends and family
S ometimes I'm organised but not always

M y eyes are like brown marbles
E nthusiastically amazing, this is me!

Elsie Dewsbury (9)
West Ashton Primary School, West Ashton

This Is Me

Teddy hoarder
Animal lover
Hedgehog admirer
Coffee maker
Sweet spotter
Shopping adorer
Dragon fruit craver
Biscuit eater
Story writer
Green tea drinker
Dumpling gobbler
Noodle slurper
A doodler
Sketcher
Coconut haired creature
Aubergine detester
Short little reader
I am a quick speaker
But a slow runner.

Nicola Plant (9)

West Ashton Primary School, West Ashton

A Cheeky Monkey!

A cheeky monkey

M inons are cool and cute
O rangutans make me laugh
N othing can stop me being me
K ind, that is me
E njoyable - time you spend with me
Y ou are different to me

I love Pokémon
S illy is what I am

M y life is great
E xcellent.

Jacob Squires (10)

West Ashton Primary School, West Ashton

This Is Me!

I'm a unique star that shines in the darkness
of the night
I'm a girl with many emotions
I'm a girl with eyes like the ground beneath me
I'm a girl with lots of potential
I'm someone with an artistic mind
I'm someone with too much energy
I have a mischievous attitude
Last but not least, I'm a girl with a caring heart.

Isabelle Foo (10)
West Ashton Primary School, West Ashton

This Is Me!

T hings cute, are the best
H aving a console is so great
I love Pokémon, what is better?
S nuggling and hugging is always so cuddly

I have an amazing life
S o it's all thanks to my brilliant family

M y parents are so lovely
E xcellent they are, I am so lucky.

Owen Squires (10)
West Ashton Primary School, West Ashton

This Is Me

T he sea is my favourite thing to paint
H ouses are my favourite thing to draw
I have a pet guinea pig
S unset red is my favourite colour

I love to read, I write too
S kies that are grey are what I dislike

M y hair is dark and curly
E arthquakes are what I fear.

Maia Hobbs (10)
West Ashton Primary School, West Ashton

This Is Me

Dream SMP fan and watcher
Music listener
Animal lover
Electronic user
Brunette haired
Sea-like eyes
Giraffe-like height
Caring, confident, kind and funny
Black and blue as favourite colours
YouTube user
TikTok scroller
Crisp craver
Aubergine despiser
I am a video gamer
And a food eater.

Jasmine Molloy (11)
West Ashton Primary School, West Ashton

I Know

I know...
I'm not as smart as Natasha
Or as heroic as Tony
I know...
I'm not amazing at science like Bruce
Or as skilled as Clint
I know...
I'm not as strong as Steve
And I'm not worthy like Thor

But that's because I'm not a fictional superhero
Because I am me!

Georgia Draper (10)
West Ashton Primary School, West Ashton

This Is Me!

T his is a poem about me and who I am
H ungry every now and then
I 'm fairly happy
S ometimes have a good laugh

I 've got £300, which is not that much
S ad half the time

M y sister is annoying
E asily gets bored.

Cameron Earl-Burke (9)
West Ashton Primary School, West Ashton

This Is Me

I am...
A footballer
An omelette eater
A Phineas and Pherb watcher
A snow fox lover
A silly friend
A good gamer
A martial arts master
An honest person
A tidy person
A happy person, most of the time
An angry boy when annoyed
A fun maker
An artist.

Arthur Thomas-Busow (9)
West Ashton Primary School, West Ashton

This Is Me

T he wild girl

H orse lover

I cy blue eyes like a sphere of ice

S our like a lemon

I love nature

S weet like sugar (if I want to be!)

M essy blonde hair like a bird's nest

E nergetic; I never rest.

Poppy Self (10)

West Ashton Primary School, West Ashton

This Is Me

T he kindest person
H elpful
I am caring to my family and friends
S weet like a jar of sugar

I like being kind
S our like a lemon

M e and my family love playing
E yes like the ocean.

Tilly Lewis (10)
West Ashton Primary School, West Ashton

This Is Me

I am a cat-loving maniac
A football master
A troublemaker
A healthy bean
A curious mind
A beat maker
A food raider
And a tea drinker

This rap is what makes me
Any remark I'm told
I don't care because this is me!

Jack Le Grys (10)
West Ashton Primary School, West Ashton

This Is Me

This is me...

A fighter
A strong and brave girl, like a white tiger
Hair like the waves in the sea
My dog is like a hero to me
I'm a believer
I'm an animal lover
And a carer for others
This is me!

Jaime Noad (10)
West Ashton Primary School, West Ashton

This Is Me

Playing with my friends
Going to golf
Having great fun

At break, playing tag
Going home to do homework
Watching a movie

Cooking a pepperoni pizza for dinner
Going to bed
Then doing it all again.

Harry Prichard (10)
West Ashton Primary School, West Ashton

This Is Me!

A kennings poem

I am a dramatic queen
A food lover
A graceful swimmer
A Roblox player
A mischievous maker
A cat lover
A cheeky monkey
A flexible gymnast
A brave dancer
A busy bee

This is me!

Evelyn Morris (10)

West Ashton Primary School, West Ashton

This Is Me!

I am...

A puppy lover
Tiny in size
Love nature
A dancer
Healthy eater
A colouring person
Enthusiastic
Funny
Kind
A strawberry eater
A quiz lover

This is me!

Kyra Husk (10)
West Ashton Primary School, West Ashton

This Is Me!

I am...
An animal lover
A book reader
A dark hair owner
Born a Cancer
A fan of ABBA
But most importantly
A modern music hater.

Charlotte Ashman (10)
West Ashton Primary School, West Ashton

My Dreams

I have a head full of things
Pizzas and purple stuff
McLarens and Ferraris
Minecraft and computer games
I have a head full of dreams
My dreams are that I can nibble on chocolate cake
As big and as brown as a tree

My dreams are that I can buy a McLaren
A car as shiny as a fresh green leaf

My dreams are that I could learn how to drive
Like a super dude who is lovely and kind

My dreams are that I can be an explorer
Who cares for the world without a doubt

My dreams are that I could change the world
And change it to a place from bad to good
To make our home the best in the universe.

Thomas Bilby (7)
Windhill21 Primary School, Bishop's Stortford

My Dog Bonnie

Bonnie is my Boston Terrier
She is black and white and brown
Like a beautiful dark rainbow
She is the same brown as a tiny hippo
But she isn't too brown
And she isn't too not brown

She isn't too big
And she isn't too short
But she has the same size head
As a tennis ball!
She has eyes like two juicy green apples
That scrunch when she is excited

She is crazy
She likes to nibble on her purple ball
She munches on my toes
And even tries to gobble my ears!

The grossest thing she does
Is sniff butts
It doesn't matter whose butt it is

All and every dog gets their butt sniffed
She even sniffed my neighbour's butt!

My whole heart
Loves her a lot
My favourite thing about her
Is her pointy pizza ears
She is a funny little dog
Who flops her ears to one side
When I call her
Little Bonnie Boo Boo
The only thing I do not like
Is when she eats her poo.

Harrison Watts (7)
Windhill21 Primary School, Bishop's Stortford

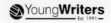

An Italian Summer

My name is Mattia
My family are Italian
I love to go on holidays
To hot, sunny, beautiful places
When the sunsets are my favourite colour
of orange
And the days are bright and hot

I love the feeling of getting on the plane
And flying high up in the baby-blue sky
Amongst the fluffy white clouds
And the sun shining yellow
Being on holiday fills me with joy
And makes my face smile as big as a
carved pumpkin
I can play with my family
Or swim in a pool
Or play with my toys
Or read my new books about pirates
and adventure
Oh, how I wish I was there!

With the night sky as inky as shadows
That is filled with hundreds of twinkling lights
and stars
The sounds of exotic foods sizzling
And the smell of delicious things to eat
As I walk past palm trees growing fruit
And gobble on sickly, sweet bubblegum ice cream
That trickles down my chin.

Mattia Rognoni (7)
Windhill21 Primary School, Bishop's Stortford

When I Grow Up!

When I grow up
I will always think about the future
And try to never think of anything sad

When I grow up
I want to only think about other things
Happy things
Wonderful things
Adventurous things
Things that will be wonderful for my life

When I grow up
I want to be someone great
Who does good for others
And helps people

When I grow up
I want to help the planet
Not just to survive
But to be kind
And help all animals to survive

When I grow up
I want to help people
To donate money to people
And to be kind

When you grow up
I hope you will be kind
And do these things too.

Jaza
Windhill21 Primary School, Bishop's Stortford

This Is Me

This is me
I'm Sophie P
Hair like mine
Ponytails
Or curly like spaghetti
Wavy and straight
Swirly and curly
It is all my style
I could even do the hair of a crocodile

I do the hair of my pet dog
No matter how much he leaps or jumps
I style my cat's hair too
A cute little bun I think she would suit
I wonder if I could plait a bird
Or put a wig on a hairless pig?

Playing with the hair of friends
I hope my love for hair will never end
I just want to scream, "Oh yeah! Oh yeah!"
Because I just really love hair!

Sophie P
Windhill21 Primary School, Bishop's Stortford

Scarlett And Her Animals

I'm Scarlett
I love to ride horses
And to play with animals
I can't be pulled away from them
No matter how hard someone might try
When I'm at home
I always play with my dog
Or my pet snail
When I'm at the stables
I love to ride my horses
I go to the yard every day
To check on the horses
Feed the horses
Ride the horses
Compete in horse shows
Enjoy pony clubs
And care for the horses
It is so fun to have pets
And I love them so much.

Scarlett Hobin-Smith (7)
Windhill21 Primary School, Bishop's Stortford

Cats, Cats, Cats,

I love cats
Big cats
Small cats
I just love them all
Cats, cats, cats
I love reading cat books
Watching cat videos
Everything cats is my thing
I love cats
They are so cute
So fluffy
So lovely

Cats, cats, cats
If I could have a cat
It would be as white as snow
With bright green eyes
Like my old cat that I miss

I also love rats
Funny that it rhymes with cats

But my dad hates rats
I guess I'll have to stick with cats
So that's that!

Emily

Windhill21 Primary School, Bishop's Stortford

Zebras

I have been thinking about zebras
People wonder if they have black stripes
Or white stripes
But they have black stripes
And white skin

My name is Carmell
I never give up on anything
I love school
It makes me happy
My favourite subject is reading
Enjoying books and writing

I am persuasive and persistent
And when I grow up
I will be a doctor
A person to make people feel better
To help people live a better life.

Carmell Stirling (7)
Windhill21 Primary School, Bishop's Stortford

My Favourite Things

Here is a list of my favourite things
Things that give me a happy grin
Like cheese sandwiches, pizza, pasta and chips
Or the colour green
My teacher, school and friends
I love the world I live in
The places I play and live

But my most favourite things are
My family, mum, dad and sister
They are my whole world
My dad loves my mum
My mum loves my sister
My sister loves me
And I love them all!

Amelia Grey (7)
Windhill21 Primary School, Bishop's Stortford

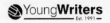

Pizza

Pizza is my favourite thing
Pizza is everything
Pizza is the most delicious food on the planet
Pizza is the tastiest food in the entire world
Pizza is the yummiest thing on Earth
In just one bite, you can taste everything
Like the scrummy taste of fresh tomato ketchup
Or the creamy taste of stringy cheese
Or the crunchy taste of the bread base
Pizza is everything!

Alfie Howard (7)
Windhill21 Primary School, Bishop's Stortford

My Dream World

I dream of imaginary worlds
Where on a sunny morning
I follow a path
That will lead to a magical place
That was so big and beautiful
A city filled with people
And delicious sweets
With clouds made of candyfloss
Juicy yummy sweeties everywhere
Instead of water
The rivers will be filled with delicious fruit
smoothies
A dream world I want to come true.

Marley Nesemann-Webb (7)
Windhill21 Primary School, Bishop's Stortford

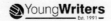

All About Kittens

Happy days
Great days are filled with cute kittens everywhere
Tickling my hands with their soft paws trying to get me to play
Soft kittens, cute kittens, lovely kittens
Miaow, miaow
Asking for toys
Purring, purring with delight
Fluffy, cuddly kittens
They are my best friends
Kittens, kittens everywhere.

Riley Edwards (7)
Windhill21 Primary School, Bishop's Stortford

Art Is Fantastic

Art is fun
Amazing
Exciting
Messy

I love to make a mess
And splash around all the colours
Sketching
Drawing
At school or at home
It is great fun

I would paint every day
With my favourite red colour
Everyone would love it
But no one would love painting
As much as me.

Farida
Windhill21 Primary School, Bishop's Stortford

All About Football

My name is Freddie
Orange is my favourite colour
Like the fur of a tiger
Or a lion's mane
Football is my favourite sport
With professional players like Kieran Tierney
Or Declan Rice
And great teams such as Man City
I love football!

Freddie
Windhill21 Primary School, Bishop's Stortford

Young Writers Est. 1991

YOUNG WRITERS INFORMATION

We hope you have enjoyed reading this book – and that you will continue to in the coming years.

If you're the parent or family member of an enthusiastic poet or story writer, do visit our website **www.youngwriters.co.uk/subscribe** and sign up to receive news, competitions, writing challenges and tips, activities and much, much more! There's lots to keep budding writers motivated!

If you would like to order further copies of this book, or any of our other titles, then please give us a call or order via your online account.

Young Writers
Remus House
Coltsfoot Drive
Peterborough
PE2 9BF
(01733) 890066
info@youngwriters.co.uk

Join in the conversation!
Tips, news, giveaways and much more!

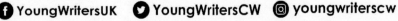
 YoungWritersUK YoungWritersCW youngwriterscw